MAKING THE GRADE ·

2

EASY POPULAR PIECES FOR YOUNG CLARINETTISTS SELECTED AND ARRANGED BY JERRY LAN

Exclusive Distributors:
Music Sales Limited
Newmarket Road, Bury St. Edmunds, Suffolk IP33 3YB.
This book © copyright 1992 Chester Music.
ISBN 0-7119-2943-2
Order No. CH60064
Cover designed by Pemberton and Whitefoord
Typeset by Pemberton and Whitefoord
Printed in the United Kingdom by
Caligraving Ltd. Thetford, Norfolk.

WARNING: the photocopying of any pages of this publication is illegal.
If copies are made in breach of copyright, the Publisher will,
where possible, sue for damages.

Chester Music

(A division of Music Sales Limited)
8/9 Frith Street, London W1V 5TZ.

INTRODUCTION

This collection of 16 popular tunes has been carefully arranged and graded to provide attractive teaching repertoire for young clarinettists. The familiarity of the material will stimulate pupils' enthusiasm and encourage their practice.

The technical demands of the solo part increase progressively up to the standard of Associated Board Grade 2. The piano accompaniments are simple yet effective and should be within the range of most pianists.

Breath marks are given throughout, showing the most musically desirable places to take a breath. Students may also need to take additional breaths when learning a piece or practising at a slower tempo, and suitable opportunities are indicated by breath marks in brackets.

GREENSLEEVES

Traditional.

This tune dates from Elizabethan times.

Notice that the Cs are sometimes sharp and sometimes natural.

© Copyright 1992 Chester Music Limited, 8/9 Frith Street, London W1.
All Rights Reserved. International Copyright Secured.

ANNIE'S SONG

Words & Music by John Denver.

'Annie's Song' was made popular as a flute solo by James Galway, but suits the clarinet equally well.

Play it as smoothly as possible, and make sure you hold all the notes for their full value.

© Copyright 1974 Cherry Lane Music Company Incorporated, USA.
Cherry Lane Music Company Limited, Ipswich, Suffolk.
All Rights Reserved. International Copyright Secured.

IMAGINE

Words & Music by John Lennon.

Notice the way the opening two-bar phrase is repeated, with slight variations.

If you have problems with bar 15, practise it slowly, counting in quavers.

Moderately slow

© Copyright 1971 Lenono Music.
Administered by BMG Music Publishing Limited, Bedford House, 69-79 Fulham High Street, London SW6.
All Rights Reserved. International Copyright Secured.

SAILING

Words & Music by Gavin Sutherland.

This was a big hit for Rod Stewart. You will need good breath control,
and you should try to avoid using the bracketed breath marks as far as possible.

Slow beat

© Copyright 1972 by Island Music Limited, London W6.
All Rights Reserved. International Copyright Secured.

MULL OF KINTYRE

Words & Music by McCartney & Laine

Look out for the quaver/dotted crotchet group in bar 4 and elsewhere,
and make sure the rhythm is really accurate. Don't be late playing the second note in bar 14.

With a lilt

© Copyright 1977 by MPL Communications Limited.
Administered by MPL Communications Limited, by arrangement with ATV Music.
All Rights Reserved. International Copyright Secured.

SKYE BOAT SONG

Traditional.

This is one of the best known Scottish melodies. It needs a sustained sound and smooth playing.

© Copyright 1992 Chester Music Limited, 8/9 Frith Street, London W1.
All Rights Reserved. International Copyright Secured.

NELLIE THE ELEPHANT

Words by Ralph Butler. Music by Peter Hart.

Watch out for the key change.
This piece starts in G minor, but the chorus is in G major.

© Copyright 1956 Dash Music Company Limited, 8/9 Frith Street, London W1.
All Rights Reserved. International Copyright Secured.

TULIPS FROM AMSTERDAM

English Words by Gene Martyn. Original Words by Neumann & Bader. Music by Ralf Arnie.

Here's a cheerful tune. It's not very difficult, but needs to swing along at a good pace.

Notice the D sharps towards the end.

© Copyright 1956 Beboton-Verlag GmbH, Germany.
Hans Sikorski Limited, 8/9 Frith Street, London W1.
All Rights Reserved. International Copyright Secured.

GREENSLEEVES

Traditional.

This tune dates from Elizabethan times.
Notice that the Cs are sometimes sharp and sometimes natural.

© Copyright 1992 Chester Music Limited, 8/9 Frith Street, London W1.
All Rights Reserved. International Copyright Secured.

ANNIE'S SONG

Words & Music by John Denver.

'Annie's Song' was made popular as a flute solo by James Galway, but suits the clarinet equally well.

Play it as smoothly as possible, and make sure you hold all the notes for their full value.

© Copyright 1974 Cherry Lane Music Company Incorporated, USA.
Cherry Lane Music Company Limited, Ipswich, Suffolk.
All Rights Reserved. International Copyright Secured.

IMAGINE

Words & Music by John Lennon

Notice the way the opening two-bar phrase is repeated, with slight variations.

If you have problems with bar 15, practise it slowly, counting in quavers.

© Copyright 1971 Lenono Music.
Administered by BMG Music Publishing Limited, Bedford House, 69-79 Fulham High Street, London SW6.
All Rights Reserved. International Copyright Secured.

SAILING

Words & Music by Gavin Sutherland.

This was a big hit for Rod Stewart. You will need good breath control,

and you should try to avoid using the bracketed breath marks as far as possible.

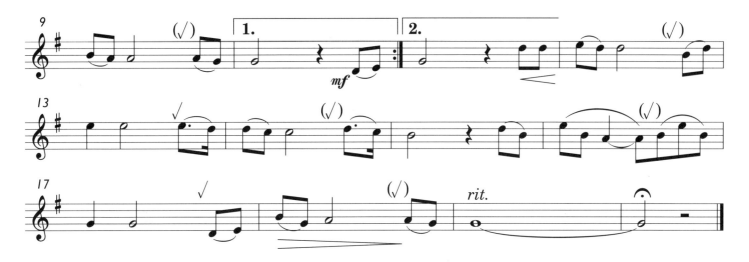

© Copyright 1972 by Island Music Limited, London W6.
All Rights Reserved. International Copyright Secured.

MULL OF KINTYRE

Words & Music by McCartney & Laine.

Look out for the quaver/dotted crotchet group in bar 4 and elsewhere,

and make sure the rhythm is really accurate. Don't be late playing the second note in bar 14.

With a lilt

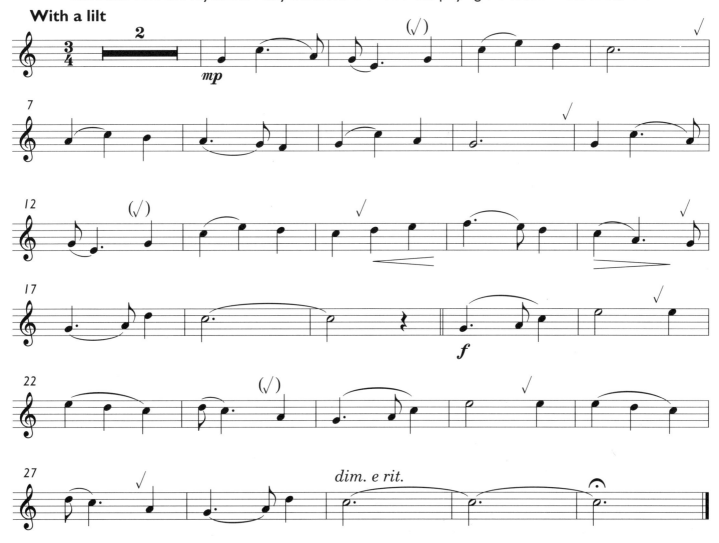

© Copyright 1977 by MPL Communications Limited.
Administered by MPL Communications Limited, by arrangement with ATV Music.
All Rights Reserved. International Copyright Secured.

SKYE BOAT SONG

Traditional.

This is one of the best known Scottish melodies. It needs a sustained sound and smooth playing.

Gently moving

© Copyright 1992 Chester Music Limited, 8/9 Frith Street, London W1.
All Rights Reserved. International Copyright Secured.

NELLIE THE ELEPHANT

Words by Ralph Butler. Music by Peter Hart.

Watch out for the key change.
This piece starts in G minor, but the chorus is in G major.

Moderately

© Copyright 1956 Dash Music Company Limited, 8/9 Frith Street, London W1.
All Rights Reserved. International Copyright Secured.

TULIPS FROM AMSTERDAM

English Words by Gene Martyn. Original Words by Neumann & Bader. Music by Ralf Arnie.

Here's a cheerful tune. It's not very difficult, but needs to swing along at a good pace.
Notice the D sharps towards the end.

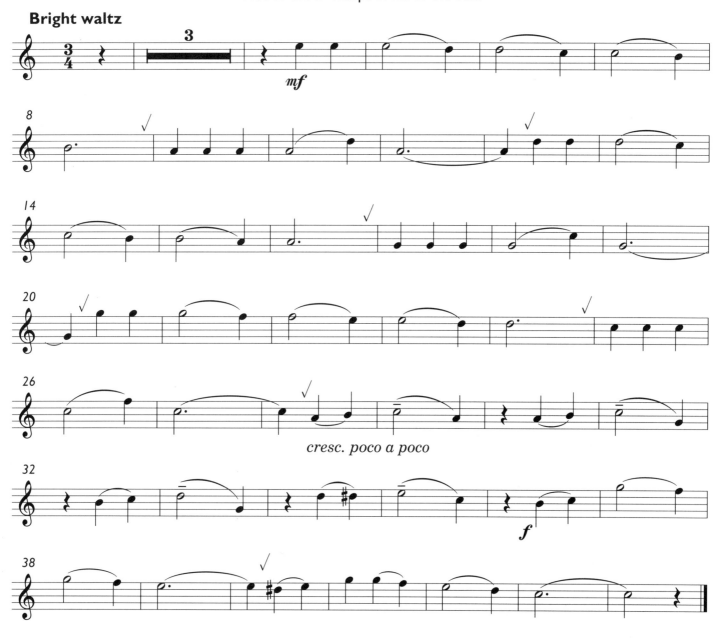

© Copyright 1956 Beboton-Verlag GmbH, Germany.
Hans Sikorski Limited, 8/9 Frith Street, London W1.
All Rights Reserved. International Copyright Secured.

AUTUMN
(FROM 'THE FOUR SEASONS')

By Antonio Vivaldi.

This theme comes from one of the most popular works in the classical repertoire.

The opening phrase is repeated *piano*, an octave lower.

© Copyright 1992 Chester Music Limited, 8/9 Frith Street, London W1.
All Rights Reserved. International Copyright Secured.

THE GIFT TO BE SIMPLE

Traditional Shaker Hymn.

Also known as 'The Lord Of The Dance', this very well known hymn tune was used by the
American composer Aaron Copland in his ballet 'Appalachian Spring'.

© Copyright 1992 Chester Music Limited, 8/9 Frith Street, London W1.
All Rights Reserved. International Copyright Secured.

BRIGHT EYES

Words & Music by Mike Batt.

This is the theme from the film 'Watership Down'. Be careful to play the rhythms accurately,
particularly the syncopated quaver/crotchet/quaver groups. Count bar 18 carefully.

© Copyright 1978 EMI Songs Limited/Watership Productions,
127 Charing Cross Road, London WC2 for the World.
All Rights Reserved. International Copyright Secured.

WHO DO YOU THINK YOU ARE KIDDING MR. HITLER?

Words by Jimmy Perry. Music by Jimmy Perry and Derek Taverner.

You will recognise this as the theme from the very popular TV series 'Dad's Army'.
Look out for the accidentals, and pay special attention to the final phrase as it crosses the break.

March tempo

© Copyright 1969 Veronica Music Limited, 8/9 Frith Street, London W1.
All Rights Reserved. International Copyright Secured.

YELLOW SUBMARINE

Words & Music by John Lennon & Paul McCartney.

This Beatles number needs to be played with a tight, accurate rhythm — don't slip into triplets in the chorus.
Notice that the verse is repeated an octave higher.

Like a march

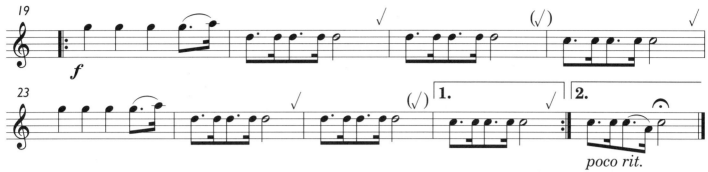

© Copyright 1966 Northern Songs, under Licence to
MCA Music Limited, 77 Fulham Palace Road, London W6.
All Rights Reserved. International Copyright Secured.

VINCENT

Words & Music by Don McLean.

Keep a steady tempo, and let the quaver passages flow smoothly.

Pay particular attention to the unusual phrasing.

© Copyright 1971, 1972 by Mayday Music Incorporated & Benny Bird Music.
MCA Music Limited, 77 Fulham Palace Road, London W6.
All Rights Reserved. International Copyright Secured.

LAST OF THE SUMMER WINE

Composed by Ronnie Hazlehurst.

This is the theme from the long-running TV series.

Look out for the E flats in bars 25 to 27 as the music modulates through C minor.

© Copyright 1973 EMI Songs Limited, 127 Charing Cross Road, London WC2.
All Rights Reserved. International Copyright Secured.

HAVAH NAGILAH

Traditional.

'Havah Nagilah' is a well-known traditional Jewish song.

Notice that C sharp is often followed by B flat (not B natural).

© Copyright 1992 Chester Music Limited, 8/9 Frith Street, London W1.
All Rights Reserved. International Copyright Secured.

10/03 (49045)

CHESTER MUSIC
(A division of Music Sales Limited)
8/9 Frith Street, London W1V 5TZ
Exclusive distributors: Music Sales Ltd., Newmarket Road
Bury St Edmunds, Suffolk IP33 3YB

Order No: CH 60064

AUTUMN
(FROM 'THE FOUR SEASONS')

By Antonio Vivaldi.

This theme comes from one of the most popular works in the classical repertoire.

The opening phrase is repeated *piano*, an octave lower.

© Copyright 1992 Chester Music Limited, 8/9 Frith Street, London W1.
All Rights Reserved. International Copyright Secured.

THE GIFT TO BE SIMPLE

Traditional Shaker Hymn.

Also known as 'The Lord Of The Dance', this very well known hymn tune was used by the
American composer Aaron Copland in his ballet 'Appalachian Spring'.

© Copyright 1992 Chester Music Limited, 8/9 Frith Street, London W1.
All Rights Reserved. International Copyright Secured.

BRIGHT EYES

Words & Music by Mike Batt.

This is the theme from the film 'Watership Down'. Be careful to play the rhythms accurately, particularly the syncopated quaver/crotchet/quaver groups. Count bar 18 carefully.

© Copyright 1978 EMI Songs Limited/Watership Productions, 127 Charing Cross Road, London WC2 for the World.
All Rights Reserved. International Copyright Secured.

WHO DO YOU THINK YOU ARE KIDDING
MR. HITLER?

Words by Jimmy Perry. Music by Jimmy Perry and Derek Taverner.

You will recognise this as the theme from the very popular TV series 'Dad's Army'.
Look out for the accidentals, and pay special attention to the final phrase as it crosses the break.

© Copyright 1969 Veronica Music Limited, 8/9 Frith Street, London W1.
All Rights Reserved. International Copyright Secured.

YELLOW SUBMARINE

Words & Music by John Lennon & Paul McCartney.

This Beatles number needs to be played with a tight, accurate rhythm — don't slip into triplets in the chorus.
Notice that the verse is repeated an octave higher.

Like a march

© Copyright 1966 Northern Songs, under Licence to
MCA Music Limited, 77 Fulham Palace Road, London W6.
All Rights Reserved. International Copyright Secured.

VINCENT

Words & Music by Don McLean.

Keep a steady tempo, and let the quaver passages flow smoothly.

Pay particular attention to the unusual phrasing.

Moderately

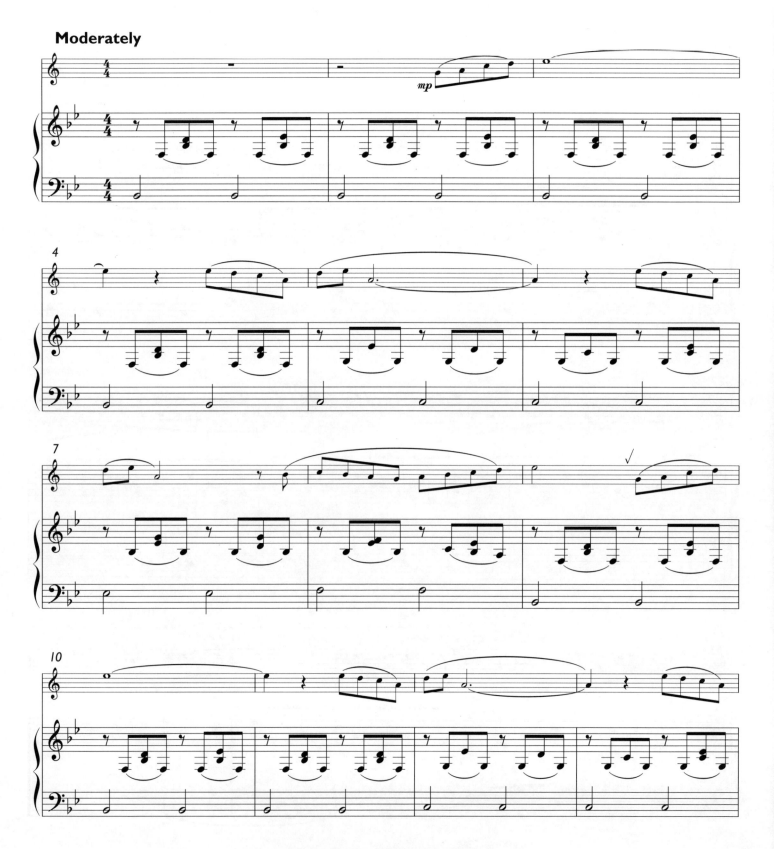

© Copyright 1971, 1972 by Mayday Music Incorporated & Benny Bird Music.
MCA Music Limited, 77 Fulham Palace Road, London W6.
All Rights Reserved. International Copyright Secured.

LAST OF THE SUMMER WINE

Composed by Ronnie Hazlehurst.

This is the theme from the long-running TV series.
Look out for the E flats in bars 25 to 27 as the music modulates through C minor.

© Copyright 1973 EMI Songs Limited, 127 Charing Cross Road, London WC2.
All Rights Reserved. International Copyright Secured.

D. 𝄋 al Fine

HAVAH NAGILAH

Traditional.

'Havah Nagilah' is a well-known traditional Jewish song.

Notice that C sharp is often followed by B flat (not B natural).

Quite fast

© Copyright 1992 Chester Music Limited, 8/9 Frith Street, London W1.
All Rights Reserved. International Copyright Secured.

10/03 (49045)